Every Day Baby

WRITTEN BY DR. AMY DEAN - TSAHEY
ILLUSTRATED BY FRANCINE C. STILL HICKS

Mynd Matters Publishing
715 Peachtree Street NE
Suites 100 & 200
Atlanta, GA 30308

ISBN: 978-1-953307-65-1 (pbk)
ISBN: 978-1-953307-66-8 (hdcv)
Library of Congress Control Number: 2021910437

Illustrated by Francine C. Still Hicks

www.amydeantsahey.com

To my great grandparents, Mama Jessie and Grandad Hirem, and grandparents, Mama Julie and Papa Neé, Margaret and Willie, Mom and Dad, and all family extended and near,
This story speaks to the child in all of us. Always allow that child to have a voice.
Remember, you have a name and YOU ARE ROYALTY.

The clock tick tick tocks. A baby is crying.

What day is it? Oh, it is a Monday.
If she is a girl, she will be called, "Adwoa."
If he is a boy, he will be called, "Kodjo."

Adwoa, Adwoa. Pretty as a shell. Adwoa, Monday, yes she is a girl!

The clock tick, tickety tocks, a baby is blowing spit.

Oh my! What day is it? It is a Tuesday.
If she is a girl, she will be called "Abena." If he is a boy, he will be called, "Kwabena."

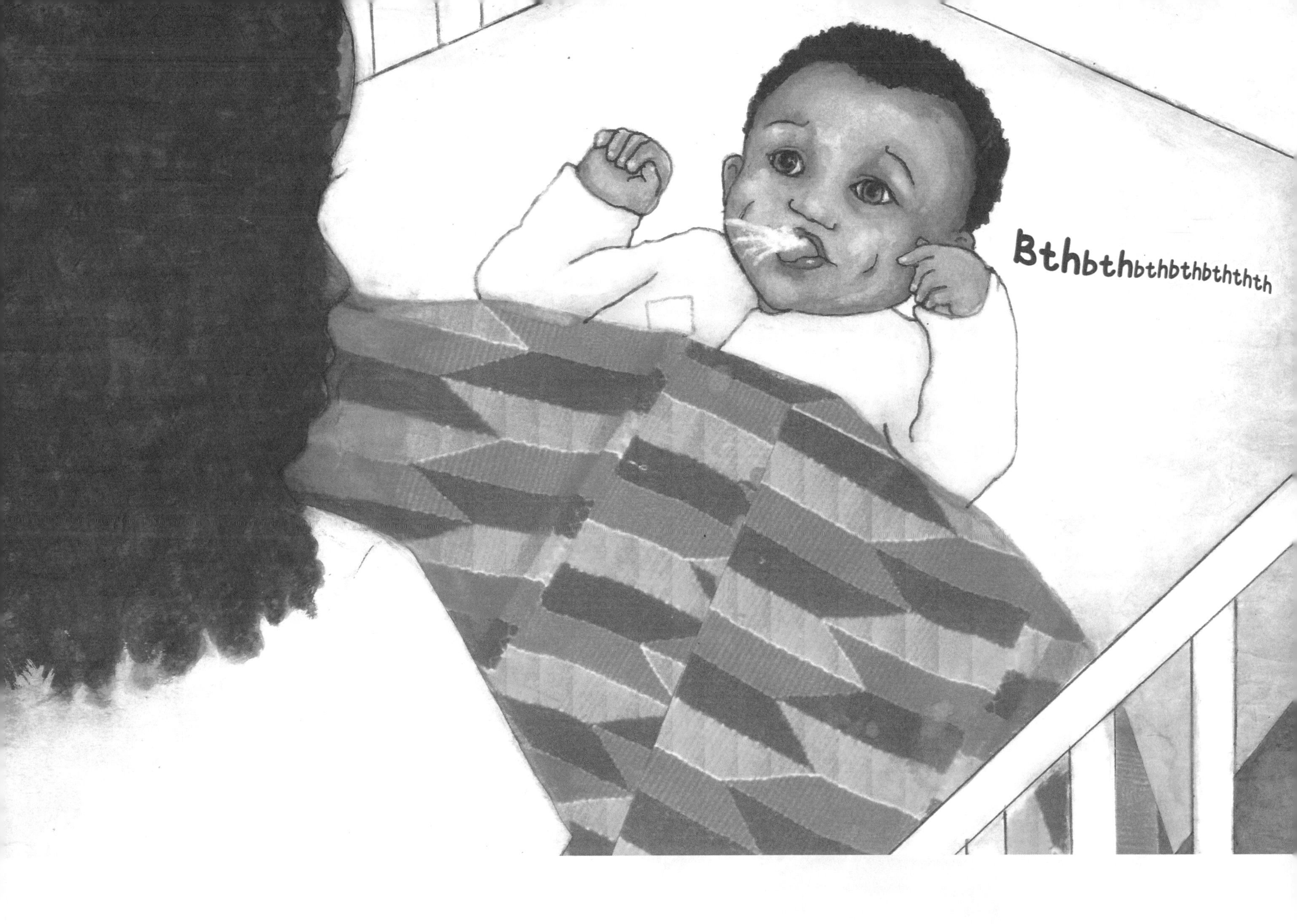

Kwabena, Kwabena, strong, what a joy! Kwabena, Tuesday, yes he is a boy!

The clock is ticking tick, tock, tick, a baby is cooing small.

Teh ha ha. What day is it?
Oh, it is a Wednesday. If she is a girl, she will be called, "Ekua" and
if he is a boy, he will be called, "Kweku."

Kweku, Kweku, he's already found his voice. Kweku, Wednesday, yes he is a boy!

Tick Tock, Tick the clock, A baby is screaming loudly.

What day is it? Oh it is a Thursday!
If she is a girl, she will be called, "Yaa" and if he is a boy, he will be called, "Yaw."

Yaa Baby, Yaa Baby, cries so much until. Yaa Baby, Thursday, yes she is a girl!

Tock, tick, tick, tock, a baby is passing gas.
Mmmmmnnnhhhh
What day is it? Oh it is a Friday! If she is a girl, she will be called "Efia" and if he is a boy, he will be called "Kofi."

Kofi, Kofi leader and much more. Kofi Friday, Yes, he is a boy.

Tick toc tick tick tock, a baby is burping or two?

Oooh, what day is this? It is a Saturday!
If she is a girl, she will be called, "Ama." If he is a boy, he will be called "Kwame."

Kwame, Ama, welcome to the world! Kwame, Ama, a boy and yes a girl!

Tick tock, the clock never stops. A baby is crying again.
What day is this?

It is a Sunday!
If she is a girl, she will be called, "Akosua." If he is a boy, he will be called "Kwasi."

Kwasi, Prince Kwasi, a great life you'll enjoy. Kwasi, Sunday and yes, he is a boy!

4 babies are born, every second or more.

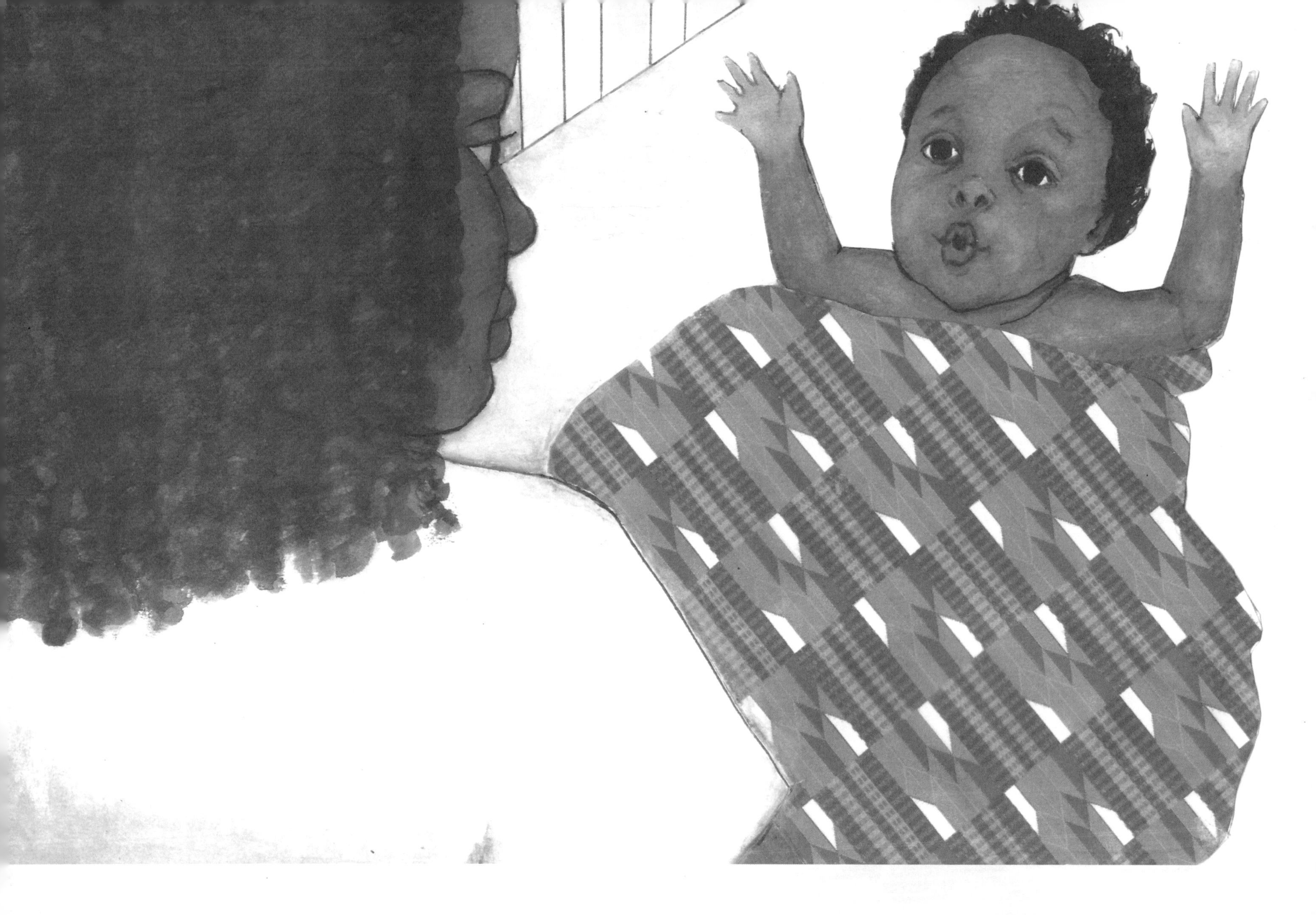

Every minute of all of our days.
Monday through Sunday...

There's no place, not one, where a baby's not born this day.

WHAT DAY WERE YOU BORN?

CPSIA information can be obtained
at www.ICGtesting.com
Printed in the USA
LVRC090822020621
689129LV00002B/35

* 9 7 8 1 9 5 3 3 0 7 6 5 1 *